D1649746

Bond Assessment Papers

Second papers in English

J M Bond and Sarah Lindsay

Key words

Some special words are used in this book. You will find them picked out in **bold** in the Papers. These words are explained here.

adjective	a word that describes somebody or something
adverb	a word that gives extra meaning to a verb
alphabetical order	words arranged in the order found in the alphabet
antonym	a word with a meaning opposite to another word *hot – cold*
compound word	a word made up of two other words *football*
conjunction	a word used to link sentences, phrases and words *and*, *but*
consonant letters	all letters of the alphabet apart from a, e, i, o, u (vowel letters)
contraction	two words shortened into one with an apostrophe placed where the letter/s have been dropped *do not = don't*
definition	meanings of words
diminutive	a word implying smallness *booklet*
homonym	words that have the same spelling as another word, but a different meaning
homophone	words that have the same sound as another but a different meaning or spelling *right / write*
noun	a word for somebody or something
collective noun	a word referring to a group *swarm*
proper noun	the names of people, places etc. *Ben*
past tense	something that has already happened
phrase	a group of words that act as a unit
adjectival phrase	a group of words describing a noun
plural	more than one *cats*
prefix	a group of letters added to the beginning of a word *un*, *dis*
present tense	something happening now
pronoun	words often replacing nouns
personal pronoun	pronouns used when writing about ourselves or others *I*, *you*, *he*
root word	words to which prefixes or suffixes can be added to make other words *quickly*
singular	one *cat*
suffix	a group of letters added to the end of a word *ly*, *ful*
syllables	the beats in a word
synonym	words with a very similar meaning to another word *quick – fast*
verb	a 'doing' or 'being' word
vowel letters	the letters a, e, i, o, u

2

Paper 1

Bed in Summer

In winter I get up at night
And dress by yellow candle-light.
In summer, quite the other way,
I have to go to bed by day.

I have to go to bed and see
The birds still hopping in the tree,
Or hear the grown-up people's feet
Still going past me in the street.

And does it not seem hard to you,
When all the sky is clear and blue,
And I should like so much to play,
To have to go to bed by day?

by Robert Louis Stevenson

Underline the right answers.

1 What does the child in the poem 'dress by'?
(torch-light, candle-light, electric-light)

2 What does the child see when he goes to bed in the summer?
(stars, people, birds)

3 What would the child rather be doing?
(sleeping, playing, walking)

3

Answer these questions.

4 Why does the child have to dress by candle-light in the winter?

_____

5 What other sounds might the child hear when lying in bed in the summer?

_____

6–7 Which two words are used to describe the sky?

_____   _____

8 Do you mind going to bed when it is light outside? Why?

_____

Underline a **noun** in each line.

9 pretty <u>book</u> went she busy

10 it large ready new <u>desk</u>

11 brown <u>Wednesday</u> ran some our

12 <u>legs</u> dirty them broken their

13 interesting <u>house</u> long dull her

14 from Hannah get <u>old</u> tipped

15 <u>paper</u> badly sad come too

Put these words in **alphabetical order**.

wrist   elbow   head   foot   arm   leg

16–21

(1) <u>arm</u>   (2) <u>elbow</u>   (3) <u>foot</u>

(4) <u>head</u>   (5) <u>leg</u>   (6) <u>wrist</u>

Add a sequence word at the beginning of each sentence so that it makes sense.

While   After   Then   First

22 <u>First</u> Tina sat in her chair while her teacher took the register.

23 <u>Then</u> she copied some sentences from the board.

24 <u>After</u> her teacher collected in the homework, Tina was writing.

25 <u>While</u> she had finished copying the sentences she was allowed out to play.

Circle the words that have two **syllables**.

26–31

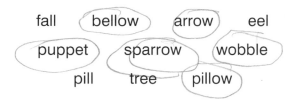

fall (bellow) (arrow) eel

(puppet) (sparrow) (wobble)

pill tree (pillow)

6

Rewrite the short passage, putting in the missing capital letters and full-stops.

32–40

mr scott visited edinburgh and glasgow each friday then he travelled on the overnight train to london

Mr Scott visited Edinburgh and Glasgow.
Each Friday then he travelled on
the overnight train to London.

9

40
TOTAL ·

Paper 2

Male and female pandas mate only a few days during the year, some time between mid-March and mid-May. In the late summer or early autumn, the mother panda finds a protected place – a hollow tree or a cave – and there she gives birth.

The newborn baby looks more like a mouse than a panda. Its tiny, pink body has just a few white hairs on it.

The mother panda gently picks up the baby with her mouth. She holds it in her paws and licks it clean. Then she puts it against her breast so that it can drink her milk.

Adapted from *Animals' World* by Jane Goodall

Underline the right answers.

1 Pandas mate some time between mid-March and (mid-April, <u>mid-May</u>, mid-June).

2 A baby panda looks like a (rat, <u>mouse</u>, cat, bear).

3 A baby panda's body is (black, <u>white</u>, brown, <u>pink</u>) when it is first born.

Answer these questions.

4–5 Which two protected places might a panda give birth in?

A hollow tree or a cave.

6 How does a panda clean her baby?

By licking it clean.

7 In which season do pandas mate?

Only a few days during the year.

Put a question mark or exclamation mark at the end of each sentence.

8 Where is your book _?_

9 Please will you help me _?_

10 Sit down at once _!_

11 Stop shouting _!_

12 What time is it _?_

13 Hurry up _!_

Underline the **verb** in each sentence.

14 The farmer <u>walked</u> in the valley.

15 He <u>drove</u> the bus into the garage.

16 Dave <u>visited</u> his new school.

17 Karen <u>watched</u> the plane through the window.

18 Mum <u>cut</u> the cake.

19 Meena <u>swam</u> in the sea.

With a line match the male and female pairs.

20 brother — lioness
21 king — sister
22 uncle — cow
23 bull — queen
24 lion — aunt
25 son — duck
26 drake — daughter

7

Add *s*, *ed* or *ing* to the **verb** in bold to complete each sentence correctly.

27 **laugh** The baby is _laughing_ out loud.

28 **run** Sam _ran_ home quickly.

29 **kick** Nick is _kicking_ the ball.

30 **wait** Jane _waited_ patiently for her brother.

31 **live** Nasar _lived_ in a huge house.

32 **crack** The trees were _cracked_ in the wind.

6

Write the **contraction** of each of these words.

Remember to add an apostrophe.

33 we are _we're_

34 it is _it's_

35 have not _haven't_

36 we will _we'll_

37 did not _didn't_

38 I am _I'm_

39 could not _couldn't_

40 you are _you're_

8

40
TOTAL

Paper 3

Early next morning Robin rose and set off, well pleased at the thought of meeting such a worthy foe. As he approached the riverside he saw, strolling along the bank, a huge and burly monk, dressed in a gown of brown cloth and with a girdle about his middle, but, unlike any other monk, he wore a knight's cap of steel upon his shaven crown. Also, there hung a sword by his side, and a large bag and bottle balanced it on the other side. Robin soon discovered the contents of the bag, for, sitting down, the monk drew a good-sized pasty from it, and, first taking a long pull at the bottle, proceeded to dispatch the pie.

Underline the right answers.

1 At what time of day is this passage set?
(morning, afternoon, evening)

2 Who did Robin see by the river?
(a foe, a knight, a monk)

3 What was the person wearing?
(a grey gown, a monk's cap, a brown gown)

Answer these questions.

4 What weapon was the monk carrying?

A sword

5 What was the monk's hair like?

_____

6 What was in the monk's bag?

_____

3

7 Why was the monk 'unlike any other monk'?

_____

8 The monk was 'strolling along the bank'. What do you think 'strolling' means?

_____

9 What do you think Robin did next?

_____

6

Underline the two **antonyms** in each line.

10 right back left correct

11 dark light day winter

12 young happy dirty clean

13 funny rich poor ill

14 danger safety crash freedom

15 here now then where

6

Add the missing commas to these sentences.

16 Diane is making a blouse a, skirt and a dress.

17–18 Steven bought some potatoes, carrots, cabbages and onions.

19–21 At school we study English, mathematics, history, geography and many other subjects.

6

Add the **suffix** _ness_ or _ment_ to each of these words.

22 weak ness   **23** agree ment

24 pay ment   **25** enjoy ness

26 blind ness   **27** state ment

28 quiet ness   **29** ill ness

8

Underline an **adjective** that best describes the word in bold.

30	**station**	three	pink	heavy	busy
31	**pencil**	wet	sharp	sleepy	dull
32	**hands**	ten	happy	clean	first
33	**June**	sunny	foggy	dark	frosty
34	**hair**	sticky	sweet	quiet	straight

5

With a number match the following words with the list of meanings.

35	carrot	_3_	(1)	a funny picture
36	carpet	_2_	(2)	he makes things out of wood
37	carton	_1_	(3)	a vegetable
38	cartoon	___	(4)	a cardboard box
39	carol	___	(5)	floor covering
40	carpenter	_4_	(6)	a song

6

40
TOTAL

Paper 4

Scene 1

Mr Williams' classroom
Writing on blackboard – 'Mr Williams is a silly old fool'

Mark and Andy are playing in Mr Williams' classroom during playtime. They should have been outside. Suddenly they hear footsteps coming down the corridor.

Mark   Quick! Hide! He is coming, I can hear his footsteps.
Andy   Where? He has eyes in the back of his head. Even if we hide he will know we are here.

Mark   We must try – what about the store cupboard?

They both rush over to the store cupboard.

Footsteps getting closer.

Mark   It's locked.
Andy   Hurry up! Under Mr Williams' table.

Mark and Andy sitting under table.

Mark   I wish I hadn't written anything on the blackboard!

Underline the right answers.

1 Which scene of the play is this?
   (Scene 1, Scene 2, don't know)

2 Whose classroom were the boys playing in?
   (Mr Williams', Mrs Williams', the headmaster's)

3 Where did the boys want to hide first?
   (behind a desk, under the teacher's table, in the store cupboard)

3

Answer these questions.

4 Why couldn't the boys hide in the cupboard?
   Because it was locked.

5 What had Mark written on the blackboard?
   Mr Williams is a silly old fool.

6 Whose footsteps do you think were coming down the corridor?
   I think it was Mr William and the class.

7 What do you think will happen next?
   I think Mark and Andy would be in trouble.

4

Write an *igh* word that matches each picture.

8 night

9 light

10  fight

11

11 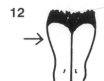   **12**    **13**

_____   _____   _____

Name the **collective noun** for each of the following.

14 twelve cows   _____

15 a large number of wasps   _____

16 a large area of trees   _____

17 a handful of flowers   _____

18 a group of sheep   _____

19 a side of football players   _____

Arrange these words in the order you would find them in the dictionary.

    colour   dark   eel   dragon   egg   change

20 (1) _____   **21** (2) _____   **22** (3) _____

23 (4) _____   **24** (5) _____   **25** (6) _____

Pat Mullins was nearly eight. She was a clumsy girl with big hands and feet, and seemed to fall over everything around her. Her light brown hair was tied into small bunches, but many strands had managed to escape from the restraining ribbons, and hung down dejectedly. She wore a patterned skirt which was too small for her, and a thick woollen sweater. Her legs, which looked blue, were bare, and on her feet were summer sandals.

Underline the right answers.

26 How old was Pat?
(seven, eight, nine)

27 What did Pat have in her hair?
(a slide, a clip, ribbons)

28 What was the weather like?
(summery, hot, wet, cold)

29 Write two words that describe Pat's legs.

blue   bare

30 What do you think 'restraining' means?

_____

31 What do you think 'dejectedly' means?

_____

Rewrite the **proper nouns** with capital letters.

swamp   birmingham   prince william   dexter

august   chester   block   monday   tap

abigail   mrs jones   magician   thursday

32 _____   **33** _____   **34** _____

35 _____   **36** _____   **37** _____

38 _____   **39** _____   **40** _____

Paper 5

Strange, strange, is the little old man
Who lives in the Grange.
Old, old, and they say that he keeps
A box full of gold.
Bowed, bowed, is his thin little back
Which once was so proud.
Soft, soft, are his steps as he climbs
The stairs to the loft.

Black, black, is the old shuttered house.
Does he sleep on a sack?
They say he does magic, that he can cast spells,
That he prowls round the garden listening for bells;
That he watches for strangers, hates every soul,
And peers with his dark eye through the keyhole.
I wonder, I wonder, as I lie in my bed,
Whether he sleeps with his hat on his head?
Is he really a magician with altar of stone
Or a lonely old gentleman left on his own?

Underline the right answers.

1 The man is (small, tall, medium height).

2 People say he keeps (jewels, gold, silver, pennies) in a box.

3 He walks upstairs (quietly, quickly, noisily).

3

Answer these questions.

4 What do people say he can do?

People can say he does magic.

5 What do people say he listens for?

He listens for bells.

6 What is a 'loft'?

A loft is a small space in the house which is a attic.

7–8 Write two words that describe the man.

_____   _____

9 What do you think the old man is?

_____

6

Add the correct **homophone** (a word that sounds the same but has a different spelling and meaning) in each sentence.

10 **hear** or **here**   I can _hear_ the train coming.

11 **write** or **right**   Sam got all the answers _right_ .

12 **stares** or **stairs**   Grandpa climbed the _stair_ one at a time.
Stairs

13 **saw** or **sore**   Kate _saw_ the horse galloping.

14 **road** or **rowed**   Tuhil and Frank _rowed_ as fast as they could.

15 **Witch** or **Which**   _which_ cake shall I have?

6

Underline the words that are spoken in these sentences.

16 "Quick, come here!" yelled the teacher.

17 "I'm waiting for my tea," answered Greg.

18 The children muttered, "Wish we didn't have to go to bed!"

19 "Shh, the baby is asleep," whispered Dad.

20 "You do look silly!" laughed Rupa.

5

Rewrite these sentences, making the **plurals singular**.

21 The trees swayed in the wind.

The tree swayed in the wind.

22–23 The boys ate the sweets.

The boy ate the sweet.

24 The barking dogs scared the girl.

The barking dogs scared the girl.

25–27 Sophie collected the ponies and led them to the buckets of food.

Sophie collected the pony and led them to the bucket of food.

7

Make eight **compound words** out of the eleven short words.

card   worm   butter   foot   cup   ball

snow   earth   post   egg   board

28 _____   29 _____

30 _____   31 _____

32 _____   33 _____

34 _____   35 _____

8

15

Write *am*, *is* or *are* in the sentence so that it makes sense.

36 They ~~is~~ are going to the beach.

37 I am really going to miss you.

38 We are going to have a ride tomorrow.

39 David _____ very upset.

40 The twins _____ sharing a bedroom.

5

40
TOTAL

Paper 6

In the quiet cul-de-sac of Franklin Place, Littlehampton, the children of Mount Rose Primary School had the shock of their lives when, without warning, their school was flooded when the River Frank burst its banks.

It had been raining hard for a few hours and the children had missed their morning and lunchtime playtimes outside. Suddenly Trevor Smith (aged 9) in Class 4L informed his teacher that water was pouring in under the door of the fire escape.

The children were told to leave the classroom quickly and quietly, put on their coats and line up by the netball pitch, the highest point at the school. Trevor Smith said, "At first I thought it was funny, then I felt a bit scared."

Headmaster, Mr John Royman, told us, "The fire brigade was called to help evacuate the school. The children were very sensible and no-one was left behind. The school is completely flooded."

All the children were sent home and the school will be closed for two weeks while everything dries out!

Underline the right answers.

1 In which town was Mount Rose Primary School?
   (Franklin, Littlehampton, Mount Rose)

2 Which class was Trevor Smith in?
   (Class 4, Class 9L, Class 4L)

3 Under what was water pouring into the classroom?
   (the window, the front doors, the fire exit)

Answer these questions.

4 Why was the fire brigade called?
   because there was a flood

5 Trevor Smith 'informed his teacher'. Write another word or phrase for
   'informed'.
   told

6–7 Write two words that describe how Trevor Smith felt.
   funny   scared

If you were one of the children at Mount Rose Primary School . . .

8–9 write two reasons why you think it is good that the school will be shut
     for two weeks.
   a) *the school if is flooded*
   b) *it will take a long time*

10–11 write two reasons why you think it is bad that the school will be shut
       for two weeks.
   a) *they wouldn't learn in two weeks time.*
   b)

Put an apostrophe in the correct place.

12 The man's hair   13 The boy's hand

14 My sister's foot   15 The baby's toy

16 The lady's basket   17 The dog's paw

17

Circle the **pronouns** in each sentence.

18–19 They thought he sang beautifully.

20–21 It was the best day he could remember.

22–23 He said she was very clever.

24–25 They screamed to make him hear.

8

Underline the **root word** (the word to which a prefix or suffix has been added to make another word) in each of these words.

26 dislike	**27** jumping	**28** unkind
29 frighten	**30** passed	**31** altogether

6

Rewrite these two sentences, adding the missing punctuation and capital letters.

32–36 david was unsure what day it was was it thursday

_____

_____

5

Underline a **synonym** for the word in bold.

37 pointed	shiny	sharp	dull	sloping
38 circle	square	peg	round	oblong
39 nation	country	ribbon	food	strip
40 busy	lazy	hard	soft	active

4

40
TOTAL

Paper 7

Cal was a boy who acted before he thought. Maybe sometimes he didn't think at all. He hit the butterfly a smack with his tennis racket, and it fell to the ground, stunned. Cal felt sorry then, perhaps, for what he had done to it, but it was too late, for he heard a tremendous clap of thunder and then he saw the Lady Esclairmonde, the queen of winged things, hovering right in his path.

She looked very frightening indeed – she was all wrapped in a cloak of grey and white feathers, she had the face of a hawk, hands like claws, a crest of flame, and her hair and ribbons and the train of her dress flew out sideways, as if a force twelve gale surrounded her. Cal could hear a fluttering sound, such as a flag or sail makes in a high wind. His own heart was fluttering inside him; he could hear that too, like a lark inside a biscuit tin.

"Why did you hit my butterfly, Cal?" asked the Lady Esclairmonde.

From *Lost – One Pair of Legs* by Joan Aiken

Underline the right answers.

1 Cal (stood on, squashed, <u>hit</u>) a butterfly.

2 Cal heard (<u>thunder</u>, singing, screaming) and then he saw Lady Esclairmonde.

3 Lady Esclairmonde had the face of a (butterfly, tiger, <u>hawk</u>).

3

Answer these questions.

4 What was Lady Esclairmonde's cloak like?

It had grey and white feathers.

5 What were Lady Esclairmonde's hands like?

It was like claws.

6 Cal could hear the fluttering of his heart. How is it described in the passage?

Like a lark inside a biscuit tin.

7 Why do you think Cal was frightened by Lady Esclairmonde?

_____

8 What do you think happened next? (The title of the book might give you a clue!)

_____

5

Add the **prefix** or **suffix** *al* to each of these words.

9 ____ways____	10 ____historic____	11 ____so____
12 ____ready____	13 ____mechanic____	14 ____medic____
15 ____accident____	16 ____though____	17 ____most____

9

19

Write each of these verbs in the **past tense**.

18 walk _____ 19 jump _____

20 pull _____ 21 sprint _____

22 push _____ 23 listen _____

Put one of the **conjunctions** in each of the spaces below.

until   although   but   because   so

24 Marianne stayed at home _____ she had a cold.

25 The sea is quite warm _____ we can go swimming.

26 Mum is going out now _____ she will be back soon.

27 Gary wore his new sweater _____ it made him too hot.

28 We will stay here _____ it is time for Mum to collect us.

Add *nch* or *tch* to make a word that matches each picture.

29

lu_____

30

i_____

31

sti_____

32

be_____

33

pi_____

34

stre_____

Using a line, match each word with its correct **definition**.

35 voyage   every year

36 remedy   a journey by sea

37 summit   a piece broken off something

38 annual   large, deep spoon

39 ladle   a cure

40 fragment   the top

Paper 8

Rosie hurried on. The pubs were further apart now and even the alleys were silent. Just the odd moggie, poor things, scavenging at the pigswill bins.

She was just bending down to stroke one when the siren went. For the third time that day. Rosie got the usual sinking feeling in her gut, but she wasn't all that worried. Air-raid sirens couldn't kill you. She listened intently, through the dying drone of the siren, for the sound of bombers' engines...

And heard nothing.

From *Blitz* by Robert Westall

Underline the right answers.

1 What was Rosie doing when the siren went?
(looking for shelter, looking in pigswill bins, <u>stroking a moggie</u>)

2 How many times had the siren gone off that day?
(1, 2, <u>3</u>, don't know)

3 Why was the siren warning people to take cover?
(<u>Bomber planes were approaching</u>, it was about to rain, it was getting dark)

3

Answer these questions.

4 How did Rosie feel when she heard the siren?

_____

5 Did Rosie hear the bombers?

_____

6 What do you think a 'moggie' is?

_____

7 Rosie 'listened intently'. What do you think this means?

_____

8 How would you feel if in wartime you heard a siren?

_____

5

Put these words in the **past tense** (when something has already happened),
e.g.   run   _ran_

9 go   _run_   **10** sing   _____

11 jump   _____   **12** fight   _____

13 buy   _____   **14** come   _____

6

Rewrite these sentences using a more interesting word than the words in
bold.

15 We had a **good** time at the party.

_____

16 My teacher is very **nice**.

_____

17–18 Daniel **got** out of the pool and **got** dressed.

_____

19 They had a **nice** day.

_____

20 Joseph was reading a **good** book.

6

_____

Make an **adverb** (a word that tells us more about a verb) out of each of these
words by adding _ly_ to each one.

21 weak_____   **22** poor_____

23 sad_____   **24** quick_____

25 kind_____   **26** clever_____

27 stupid_____   **28** rough_____

8

Many railway lines link London with other parts of the country. There are two main lines to Scotland: one goes up the east side of the country through York and Newcastle, and the other goes up the west side, passing through Crewe and Carlisle. If you are travelling to North Wales you leave the main line at Crewe. There are fast trains from Liverpool, Manchester and Sheffield to London and it is much easier to travel from north to south than it is to travel from east to west. There is a fast service from London to the West Country which passes through Salisbury and Exeter. There is an excellent electric service between London and south-east England.

Underline the right answers.

29–30 Which two towns would you pass through if you were travelling to Scotland on the east side of the country?
(Crewe, <u>York</u>, Salisbury, Manchester, Carlisle, <u>Newcastle</u>)

31 Which direction is it easier to travel in?
(east to west, <u>north to south</u>)

3

Answer these questions.

32 If you were travelling to North Wales, where do you leave the main line?
You will leave the main line at Crewe.

33–34 Name two cities that have fast trains to London.
Salisbury   Exeter

35 What is the service like between London and south-east England?
There is ~~one~~ an electric

4

Add the missing commas to these sentences where a short pause or pauses are needed.

36–37 Harry a very nervous boy, hated the thunder storm.

38 The boys set off along the track anxious, to get to the next village before dark.

39 Najib ran as fast as he could, barely taking a breath.

40 Leena was starving, having not had anything to eat all day.

5

40
TOTAL

Paper 9

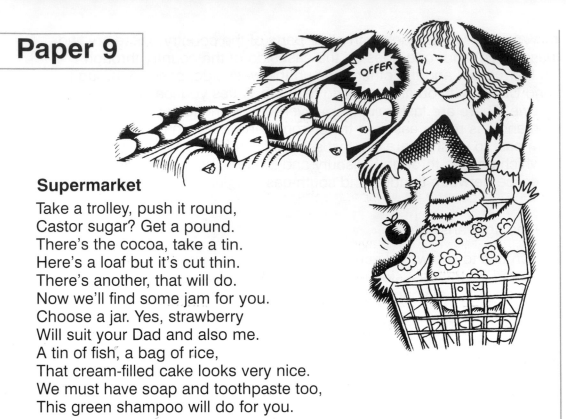

Supermarket

Take a trolley, push it round,
Castor sugar? Get a pound.
There's the cocoa, take a tin.
Here's a loaf but it's cut thin.
There's another, that will do.
Now we'll find some jam for you.
Choose a jar. Yes, strawberry
Will suit your Dad and also me.
A tin of fish, a bag of rice,
That cream-filled cake looks very nice.
We must have soap and toothpaste too,
This green shampoo will do for you.

by Barbara Ireson

Underline the right answers.

1 What is the first thing that is put in the trolley?
(castor sugar, cocoa, shampoo)

2 Do they like thin-cut bread?
(yes, no, don't know)

3 What did they buy a bag of?
(cocoa, fish, rice)

Answer these questions.

4 Who likes strawberry jam?

Dad and also me

5 What type of shop is the poem set in?

Supermarket

6 How many items did they buy?

10 things

3

7 Do you think they needed a trolley or could they have managed with a basket?

trolley

8 Do you enjoy going shopping for food? Why?

No, because it's boring

5

Write the missing **noun** with an apostrophe to show something belongs to someone.

9 The rabbit belonged to David. It was *David's* rabbit.

10 The crayons belonged to Jane. They were *Jane's* crayons.

11 The jacket belonged to Helen. It was *Helen's* jacket.

12 The bone belonged to Mop the dog. It was *Mop's* bone.

13 The rat belonged to Rick. It was *Rick's* rat.

14 The books belonged to Ann. They were *Ann's* books.

6

Write these words in **alphabetical order**.

flag   flute   flight   flesh   flood

15 _____   **16** _____   **17** _____

18 _____   **19** _____

5

Circle the **nouns** that don't have a different plural form.

20–23   reindeer   gate   grapefruit   jacket

goldfish   fork   sheep   button

4

Underline the word that has a similar meaning to the word in bold.

24 aid	act	hinder	<u>help</u>	stop
25 drop	rain	prod	bounce	<u>fall</u>
26 sad	strict	<u>unhappy</u>	glad	ugly
27 quick	loud	<u>fast</u>	slow	quiet
28 several	<u>few</u>	both	some	none
29 enjoy	hate	like	suffer	drive

25

30 **modern**   new   old   ancient   great

31 **depart**   post   leave   come   send

8

Write the **plural** of each of these **nouns** ending in *f*.

32 hoof   _____   **33** shelf   _____

34 loaf   _____   **35** calf   _____

36 leaf   _____   **37** wolf   _____

6

Write an interesting sentence about each of the following.

38 your home

_____

39 your hair

_____

40 your teacher

_____

3

40
TOTAL

Paper 10

Making a strawberry milkshake

You need: a glass
              spoon
              milk
              strawberry milkshake powder
              ice-cream
              whipped cream
              a strawberry

- Place two heaped spoonfuls of the milkshake powder in the glass.
- Add the milk so that the glass is three-quarters full.
- Mix the milk and milkshake powder with a spoon.
- Then put a large spoonful of ice-cream in the glass and again mix.
- Put some cream on the drink and finally place a strawberry on top for decoration.

Read the recipe above and then write **true** or **false** against each of these sentences.

1 You need chocolate milkshake powder to make this recipe. *false*

2 You make the drink in a glass. *true*

3 You place two level spoonfuls of milkshake powder in the glass. *false*

4 You add milk to the top of the glass. *false*

5 A large spoonful of ice-cream is added. *true*

6 You put a strawberry on top and then add the cream. *false*

7 The strawberry is for decoration. *true*

8 The spoon is for stirring the milkshake with. *true*

8

Rewrite the sentences with a more powerful **verb** for each of the verbs in bold.

9 Harry **walked** to Gary's house.

_____

10 "May I have a cake?" **said** Meena.

_____

11 Dave **took** his pen back from Ann.

_____

12 "Please can I watch television?" **said** Nigel.

_____

13 The dog **ran** around in the park.

_____

5

Match the words below with the words that have the same letter string (group of letters) but which make a different sound.

good   crown   tough   bead   height   hint

14 pint _____   **15** head _____

16 grown _____   **17** brood _____

18 through _____   **19** weight _____

6

The following sentences are not in the right order. Read them through carefully, and then write the numbers to show their correct order.

20 _____   (1) The cyclist lay on the road.

21 _____   (2) Then the policeman called for an ambulance.

22 _____   (3) A cyclist was knocked off his bicycle.

23 _____   (4) Finally the cyclist was taken to hospital.

24 _____   (5) Meanwhile a policeman arrived.

25 _____   (6) Next the ambulance arrived.

6

With a line join each word with its **diminutive** (word implying smaller version).

26 owl   duckling

27 cat   piglet

28 goose   owlet

29 pig   bullock

30 duck   kitten

31 bull   gosling

6

Rewrite the sentences, adding in the missing punctuation and capital letters.

32–35 the plane landed at heathrow airport a little late

_____

36–40 tessa and claire were very excited they were meeting their grandparents

_____

9

40
TOTAL

Paper 11

Grey as a mouse,
Big as a house,
Nose like a snake,
I make the earth shake,
As I tramp through the grass;
Trees crack as I pass,
With horns in my mouth

I will walk in the South,
Flapping big ears,
Beyond count of years
I stump round and round
Never lie on the ground
Not even to die.

From 'Oliphaunt' by J R R Tolkien

Underline the right answers.

1 What colour is the animal in the poem? (black, grey, brown, white)

2 What is this animal as big as? (a boat, a house, a mouse)

3 How does this animal go through the grass? (jumps, walks, runs)

| | 3 |

Answer these questions.

4 What does this animal never do?

Lie on the ground.

5 What animal do you think this poem is about?

Elephant

6 What do you think 'beyond count of years' means?

_____

7 Why is this animal's nose described as being like a snake?

Because elephant's nose is long like a snake.

8 Why do you think 'Trees crack as I pass'?

_____

| | 5 |

Write the two words each of these **contractions** is made from.

9 should've Should   10 won't _____

11 I'll _____   12 can't _____

13 they've _____   14 isn't _____

15 wouldn't _____   16 haven't _____

| | 8 |

Add the missing speech marks to these sentences.

17 Have you found the dog? asked Jim.

18 Let's go and play in the park, suggested Aman.

19 I don't think you have washed your face! joked Dad.

20 Are you enjoying the pizza? asked the waitress.

21 I wish it would stop raining, sighed Amy.

22 Where do you think you are going? asked Mrs Thrower.

Rewrite the word adding the **suffix** *ible* or *able*. (Remember, if the last letter of the word is a vowel, the last letter is usually dropped before adding the suffix.)

23 suit _____   **24** reason _____

25 sense _____   **26** believe _____

27 wash _____   **28** response _____

6

Underline the **adverbs** in these sentences.

29 The old man shouted angrily at the children.

30 The child ran noisily along the corridor.

31 The cat slowly stretched her leg.

32 Billy neatly wrote the date at the top of the page.

33 The robin sang sweetly as the snow fell.

34 My Dad snored loudly in front of the television.

6

With a line, match a word in each column to make a **compound word**. Write the compound words.

egg	room	**35–40** _____
moon	fall	_____
some	cup	_____
water	light	_____
drain	where	_____
class	pipe	_____

6

40 TOTAL

Paper 12

If you want to keep a pet, you should think carefully about how you will need to look after it. Animals have feelings, just as we do, and it is cruel to keep a pet if you don't have the time or money to look after it. A dog, for instance, needs lots of food, which can cost a lot of money each week. Also, you must take it for a walk, at least once every day. A cat eats less food, and can take itself out, but you must still feed it twice a day and look after it.

Animals in cages – rabbits, guinea pigs, birds, mice – need to have their cages cleaned regularly! So think carefully before you buy a pet.

Underline the right answers.

1 Do animals have feelings? (yes, no, don't know)

2 Which of the animals in the passage needs the most food?
(rabbit, dog, cat)

3 How often should you take a dog for a walk?
(at least once a week, at least once a month, at least once a day)

> 3

Answer these questions.

4 5 What two things do you need to look after a pet?

6 Which animals live in cages?

7 Write a good title for this passage.

8 If you were able to have a pet, which one would you choose? Why?

> 5

Underline all the **proper nouns** (those which should start with a capital letter).

9–16 ten   thursday   river thames   cat   kate   lunch

queen elizabeth   tonight   jake   mr norton

september   line   london

> 8

Write two sentences for each **homonym**. In each sentence the homonym must have a different meaning.

17–18 fly

_____

_____

19–20 match

_____

_____

21–22 chest

_____

_____

6

Add *its* or *it's* to fill the gap in each sentence. Don't forget to use a capital letter where necessary.

23 The cat jumped out of _____ bed.

24 "_____ time we went to school," called Mum.

25 The elephant drank through _____ trunk.

26 "_____ Sophie at the door, Amy," Dad shouted.

27–28 "_____ autumn and time the tree lost _____ leaves," commented Nathan.

6

Find eight words in the wordsearch ending in *ild* or *ind*.

b	c	h	i	l	d	t
l	g	k	n	d	s	a
i	g	o	w	t	j	f
n	r	f	i	i	h	i
d	m	i	l	d	n	n
k	i	n	d	s	e	d
s	b	e	h	i	n	d

29–36 hind   hild   blind   kind

mild   find   wild

8

Add the missing **consonant letters** to each word to make a wild animal.

37 e_ e_ _ a_ _   **38** _ io_

39 e_ u   **40** _ i_ a_ _ e

4

40 TOTAL

Some questions will be answered in the children's own words. Answers to these questions are given in *italics*. Any answers that seem to be in line with these should be marked correct.

Paper 1

1 candle-light
2 birds
3 playing
4 *It is dark outside on winter mornings*
5 *e.g. people talking, birds chirping, children playing*
6–7 clear, blue
8 *[sentence describing how they feel about going to bed when it is light outside]*
9 book
10 desk
11 Wednesday
12 legs
13 house
14 Hannah
15 paper
16 arm
17 elbow
18 foot
19 head
20 leg
21 wrist
22 First
23 Then
24 While
25 After
26–31 bellow, arrow, puppet, sparrow, wobble, pillow
32–40 **M**r **S**cott visited **E**dinburgh and **G**lasgow each **F**riday. **T**hen he travelled on the overnight train to **L**ondon.

Paper 2

1 mid-May
2 mouse
3 pink
4–5 *It gives birth in a hollow tree or a cave*

6 *She licks it*
7 *Spring*
8 ?
9 ?
10 !
11 !
12 ?
13 !
14 walked
15 drove
16 visited
17 watched
18 cut
19 swam
20 brother – sister
21 king – queen
22 uncle – aunt
23 bull – cow
24 lion – lioness
25 son – daughter
26 drake – duck
27 laughing
28 runs
29 kicking
30 waited or waits
31 lives or lived
32 cracking
33 we're
34 it's
35 haven't
36 we'll
37 didn't
38 I'm
39 couldn't
40 you're

Paper 3

1 morning
2 a monk
3 a brown gown
4 *a sword*
5 *shaven*
6 *a good-sized pasty*
7 *He wore a knight's cap*
8 *e.g. walking slowly*

9 *[sentence describing what they thought Robin did next]*
10 right, left
11 dark, light
12 dirty, clean
13 rich, poor
14 danger, safety
15 now, then
16 Diane is making a blouse, a skirt and a dress.
17–18 Steven bought some potatoes, carrots, cabbages and onions.
19–21 At school we study English, mathematics, history, geography and many other subjects.
22 weakness
23 agreement
24 payment
25 enjoyment
26 blindness
27 statement
28 quietness
29 illness
30 busy
31 sharp
32 clean
33 sunny
34 straight
35 (3)
36 (5)
37 (4)
38 (1)
39 (6)
40 (2)

Paper 4

1 Scene 1
2 Mr Williams'
3 in the store cupboard
4 *It was locked*

5 'Mr Williams is a silly old fool'
6 [the person they think is coming down the corridor]
7 [what they think happens next]
8 night
9 light
10 fight
11 right
12 thigh
13 high
14 herd
15 swarm
16 forest
17 bunch
18 flock
19 team
20 change
21 colour
22 dark
23 dragon
24 eel
25 egg
26 seven
27 ribbons
28 cold
29 blue, bare
30 *holding back*
31 *in low spirits, fed up*
32–40
Birmingham, Prince William, Dexter, August, Chester, Monday, Abigail, Mrs Jones, Thursday

Paper 5

1 small
2 gold
3 quietly
4 *He can do magic, cast spells*
5 *He listens for bells*
6 *It is the room at the top of the house*
7–8 *e.g. old, strange, little, thin, lonely*
9 *a magician or an old gentleman*
10 hear
11 right

12 stairs
13 saw
14 rowed
15 Which
16 "Quick, come here!" yelled the teacher.
17 "I'm waiting for my tea," answered Greg.
18 The children muttered, "Wish we didn't have to go to bed!"
19 "Shh, the baby is asleep," whispered Dad.
20 "You do look silly!" laughed Rupa.
21 The tree swayed in the wind.
22–23
The boy ate the sweet.
24 The barking dog scared the girl.
25–27
Sophie collected the pony and led it to the bucket of food.
28–35
e.g. cardboard, earthworm, buttercup, football, snowball, postcard, eggcup, cupboard, snowboard, footboard
36 are
37 am
38 are
39 is
40 are

Paper 6

1 Littlehampton
2 Class 4L
3 the fire exit
4 *to help evacuate the school*
5 *told, said to*
6–7 *amused, excited, scared, frightened*
8–9 *extra holiday, no work, no homework etc.*
10–11
get behind in work, miss friends, miss teacher etc.
12 The man's hair
13 The boy's hand

14 My sister's foot
15 The baby's toy
16 The lady's basket
17 The dog's paw
18–19
They, he
20–21
It, he
22–23
He, she
24–25
They, him
26 dis*like*
27 *jumping*
28 un*kind*
29 *frighten*
30 *passed*
31 al*together*
32–36
David was unsure what day it was. **W**as it **T**hursday**?**
37 sharp
38 round
39 country
40 active

Paper 7

1 hit
2 thunder
3 hawk
4 *It was a cloak of grey and white feathers*
5 *Her hands were like claws*
6 *'like a lark inside a biscuit tin'*
7 *She looked very frightening; his heart was fluttering inside him*
8 *Lady Esclairmonde took away Cal's legs*
9 always
10 historical
11 also
12 already
13 mechanical
14 medical
15 accidental
16 although
17 almost
18 walked

19 jumped
20 pulled
21 sprinted
22 pushed
23 listened
24 because
25 so
26 but/although
27 although/but
28 until
29 lunch
30 itch
31 stitch
32 bench
33 pinch
34 stretch
35 voyage – a journey by sea
36 remedy – a cure
37 summit – the top
38 annual – every year
39 ladle – large, deep spoon
40 fragment – a piece broken off something

Paper 8

1 stroking a moggie
2 3
3 Bomber planes were approaching
4 *She was fed up but not that worried*
5 *No, she heard nothing*
6 *cat*
7 *listened carefully*
8 *[own feelings about hearing a siren in wartime]*
9 went
10 sang
11 jumped
12 fought
13 bought
14 came
15 *e.g. great*
16 *e.g. thoughtful*
17–18
    e.g. jumped, quickly
19 *e.g. lovely*
20 *e.g. brilliant*
21 weakly

22 poorly
23 sadly
24 quickly
25 kindly
26 cleverly
27 stupidly
28 roughly
29–30
    York, Newcastle
31 north to south
32 *at Crewe*
33–34
    any two of: Liverpool, Manchester, Sheffield, Salisbury, Exeter
35 *It is an excellent electric service*
36–37
    Harry, a very nervous boy, hated the thunder storm.
38 The boys set off along the track, anxious to get to the next village before dark.
39 Najib ran as fast as he could, barely taking a breath.
40 Leena was starving, having not had anything to eat all day.

Paper 9

1 castor sugar
2 no
3 rice
4 *They all like strawberry jam*
5 *It is set in a supermarket*
6 *They bought 10 items*
7 *They could have managed with a basket (just)*
8 *[answer describing whether they like shopping for food and why]*
9 It was David's rabbit.
10 They were Jane's crayons.
11 It was Helen's jacket.
12 It was Mop's bone.
13 It was Rick's rat.
14 They were Ann's books.
15 flag

16 flesh
17 flight
18 flood
19 flute
20–23
    reindeer, grapefruit, goldfish, sheep
24 help
25 fall
26 unhappy
27 fast
28 some
29 like
30 new
31 leave
32 hooves
33 shelves
34 loaves
35 calves
36 leaves
37 wolves
38 *[an interesting sentence about their home]*
39 *[an interesting sentence about their hair]*
40 *[an interesting sentence about their teacher]*

Paper 10

1 False
2 True
3 False
4 False
5 True
6 False
7 True
8 True
9 *strolled*
10 *pleaded*
11 *grabbed*
12 *nagged*
13 *sprinted*
14 hint
15 bead
16 crown
17 good
18 tough
19 height
20 3

21 1
22 5
23 2
24 6
25 4
26 owl – owlet
27 cat – kitten
28 goose – gosling
29 pig – piglet
30 duck – duckling
31 bull – bullock
32–35
    The plane landed at **H**eathrow **A**irport a little late**.**
36–40
    Tessa and **C**laire were very excited**. T**hey were meeting their grandparents**.**

Paper 11

1 grey
2 a house
3 walks
4 It never lies on the ground
5 *It is about an elephant*
6 *It is so old that it has lost count.*
7 *Elephants have long noses, like the body of a snake*
8 *Elephants are so strong they can break branches as they walk past trees*
9 should have
10 will not
11 I will/I shall
12 cannot
13 they have
14 is not
15 would not
16 have not
17 "Have you found the dog?" asked Jim.
18 "Let's go and play in the park," suggested Aman.
19 "I don't think you have washed your face!" joked Dad.
20 "Are you enjoying the pizza?" asked the waitress.

21 "I wish it would stop raining," sighed Amy.
22 "Where do you think you are going?" asked Mrs Thrower.
23 suitable
24 reasonable
25 sensible
26 believable
27 washable
28 responsible
29 angrily
30 noisily
31 slowly
32 neatly
33 sweetly
34 loudly
35–40
    eggcup, moonlight, somewhere, waterfall, drainpipe, classroom

Paper 12

1 yes
2 dog
3 at least once a day
4–5 *time and money*
6 *rabbits, guinea-pigs, birds, mice*
7 *Keeping Pets, Pets Need Time and Money*
8 *[answer stating a pet they would choose and reason why]*
9–16
    Thursday, River Thames, Kate, Queen Elizabeth, Jake, Mr Norton, September, London
17–18
    [two sentences, each using different meaning of homonym fly]
19–20
    [two sentences, each using different meaning of homonym match]
21–22
    [two sentences, each using different meaning of homonym chest]

23 its
24 It's
25 its
26 It's
27–28
    It's, its
29–36
    child, blind, mild, kind, behind, find, wind, wild
37 elephant
38 lion
39 emu
40 giraffe

Paper 13

1 a merry-go-round
2 scarlet
3 on their necks
4–5 *white teeth and red tongues*
6 *Matthew's elbow*
7 *excitement*
8 *excited, scared, worried, happy*
9 scene
10 seen
11 bough
12 bow
13 hole
14 whole
15 meat
16 meet
17 the girl's jeans
18 my father's shoe
19 the child's toy
20 the dog's paw
21 Ravi's pencil
22 my gran's bracelet
23 station
24 stem
25 stick
26 storm
27 stranger
28 study
29 shaggy
30–31
    bright blue
32 glistening
33 cosy

34–35
   long, golden
36 *e.g. shout*
37 *e.g. stare*
38 *e.g. stroll*
39 *e.g. scream*
40 *e.g. feel*

Paper 14

1. cold and misty
2. the bees
3. Rabbit's house
4. *They weren't making honey*
5. *He was worried about being lost on the top of the forest*
6. *Tigger*
7. *They would hurry away in a different direction*
8. *e.g. upset, lonely, frightened, hurt*

9–10
   kindness, kindly

11–12
   blindness, blinding, blinded, blindly (any 2)

13–14
   jumped, jumping

15–16
   correctness, corrected, correcting, correctly (any 2)

17–18
   The **knives are** sharp.

19–20
   The **women** picked up the **children**.

21–22
   The **leaves were** yellow.

23–26
   Your **feet are** too big for **these slippers**.

27–29
   Adventures at **L**ongley **F**arm

30–31
   Flying **M**achines

32 *He/She is looking for a partner to sit next to on the coach*
33 *a coach*
34 *no*

35 *e.g. lonely, upset*
36 *e.g. fun*
37 *e.g. great*
38 *e.g. smart*
39 *e.g. received*
40 *e.g. grabbed*

Paper 15

1. a dog
2. picking strawberries
3. the sky
4. *to play a game*
5. *'king of the skies'*
6. *The Golden Eagle might grab one*
7. *prey*

8–9 *e.g. concerned, frightened, terrified*

10–15
   "**H**ave you seen my hat**?**" called Wendy**,** going to the door**.**

16. the three dogs' collars
17. the five girls' socks
18. the nine hens' eggs
19. the two cats' bowls
20. the four dolls' beds
21. the five boys' footballs
22. the three spiders' webs

23–24
   e.g. slowly, quickly

25–26
   e.g. peacefully, silently

27–28
   e.g. messily, quickly

29–30
   e.g. carefully, hastily

31. wasp
32. water
33. watch
34. swamp
35. swan
36. dropped
37. hurry
38. different
39. under
40. select

Paper 16

1. They hover
2. £99.99
3–4 *Walking won't be an effort. They are comfortable.*
5. *'The Latest in Footwear'*
6. *To encourage people to buy them, to be trendy like others*
7. *[answer stating whether they would like a pair of Hover Shoes and why]*
8. bananas
9. foxes
10. lorries
11. trays
12. churches
13. brushes
14. girls
15. beaches
16. We must get in the car, otherwise we will get wet.
17. Daniel's grandmother could do a little magic, but not much.
18. She was very unhappy, but her face didn't show it.
19. The dog ran on ahead, desperately looking for his home.
20. Fran dozed off, her eyes drowsy with sleep.
21. Groping in the dark, Sam found the light switch.
22. princess
23. duchess
24. wife
25. aunt
26. she
27. niece
28. sister
29. The <u>large, brown</u> clock hung on the wall.
30. The <u>bright, loud, flashing</u> fireworks exploded in the air.
31. Sam, <u>the long-haired, shaggy</u> dog loved going for a walk.
32. The <u>stern, pale-faced</u> teacher glared at the children.
33. Caroline's coat, <u>soaked and muddy</u>, didn't look new any more.

34 Rain poured from the <u>grey, heavy</u> clouds.

35 [a sentence including the pronoun, I]

36 [a sentence including the pronoun, ours]

37 [a sentence including the pronoun, him]

38 [a sentence including the pronoun, mine]

39 [a sentence including the pronoun, they]

40 [a sentence including the pronoun, she]

Paper 17

1–2 on the backs of animals, in a tent

3 Fritz

4 Jack

5 They were coaxed in with handfuls of corn

6 The dogs bought them back into line

7 people / animals moving in a line

8 to keep all the animals together / there were so many of them they couldn't travel fast

9–16 gatepost, bunch, Wednesday, Tom, Edinburgh, Edward, freedom, stream

17 "Come quickly!" screamed Sam.

18 "How are you, Gran?" asked Peter.

19 "It's time to go," sighed Mum.

20 "This way to the Tunnel of Screams," directed the attendant.

21 "Have we got time?" enquired Nancy.

22 "Where are my slippers?" exclaimed Grandad.

23 stiffly

24 gently

25 loudly

26 cheerfully

27 roughly

28 expression

29 instruction

30 subtraction

31 collision

32 education

33 pollution

34 e.g. sad

35 e.g. small

36 e.g. drop

37 e.g. quiet

38 e.g. thick/fat

39 e.g. below

40 e.g. up

Paper 18

1 False

2 True

3 False

4 True

5 True

6 False

7 False

8 True

9 True

10 although

11 than

12 so

13 but/although

14 if

15 and/so

16 bub/ble

17 pad/dle

18 flan/nel

19 ken/nel

20 ar/rive

21 sad/dle

22 bur/row

23 cab/bage

24–31

	add 'er'	add 'est'
short	shorter	shortest
high	higher	highest
small	smaller	smallest
slow	slower	slowest

32 mince

33 minister

34 mint

35 minute

36 snow – cow

37 pull – skull

38 ear – wear

39 wave – have

40 bough – trough

Paper 19

1 no

2 some of them

3 Billy

4–5 They call him names. They make jokes about his mum

6 They don't really mean it

7–9 e.g. lonely, upset, sad, angry

10 hand + bag

11 sun + light

12 candle + stick

13 shoe + lace

14 tooth + paste

15 dust + bin

16 post + man

17–22

re	de	pre
replay	deflate	prehistoric
revisit	demist	precaution

23–24
[a sentence including the phrase, this bird's chicks]

25–26
[a sentence including the phrase, that girl's sweets]

27–28
[a sentence including the phrase, those boys' pencils]

29–33
<u>Antony likes playing football.</u>
<u>Brian likes painting.</u>
<u>Brian likes craft lessons.</u>
<u>The other boys like Antony.</u>
<u>Antony would rather play cricket than stay indoors.</u>

34–40

nouns – Thursday, scream
adjectives – windy, loud
verbs – walking, heard
adverbs – briskly

Paper 20

1 market
2 tinsel
3 the fairy
4 *She got them from the loft*
5 *The fairy lights were put on first*
6 *She was very fond of the coloured glass balls*
7–8 e.g. happy, excited
9 [a number of festivals, many religious e.g. Diwali]
10 aircraft
11–12
fish, seaweed
13 bison
14 sheep
15 bridge
16 judge
17 hedge
18 badge
19 fridge
20 lodge
21 !
22 ?
23 !
24 ?
25 ?
26 !
27 !
28 ?
29–34
camcorder, CD player, cinema, astronaut, television, microwave

35–40

Pronouns about others	Pronouns about myself
yours	me
hers	I
theirs	mine

Paper 21

1–2 salt, fat
3 hand-hot
4–5 sugar, yeast
6–7 *set aside the yeast mixture, knead the dough*
8 *It needs to be put in an oven and baked*
9–10
Aman has to buy carrots, potatoes, rice and tomatoes at the shop.
11–13
At the park Geri, Meena, David, Jason and John all play together.
14–15
On Mark's way to school he passes the police station, the swimming pool, the park and the shops.
16–17
At the farm the children fed the goats, stroked the pigs, milked the cows and brushed the horse.
18–25

	add 'er'	add 'est'
hot	hotter	hottest
tall	taller	tallest
big	bigger	biggest
thin	thinner	thinnest

26 droplet
27 duckling
28 bullock
29 booklet
30–35
"Is it time Jess got out of bed?" asked her brother.
36 their
37 There
38–39
Their, there
40 There

Paper 22

1–2 an egg-shell, a coconut
3 Rushing waves
4 *horses' hooves*
5 *a giant's voice*
6–7 *listened, thought, could, hear, held, heard, hatching, found, pounding, took, see, might, booming (any two of these verbs)*
8 *Chicks peck their way out of egg-shells when they are born*
9 friendship
10 neighbourhood
11 motherhood
12 apprenticeship
13 It's
14 its
15–16
It's, it's
17 its
18 its
19 It's
20 It's
21 [a phrase describing a coat]
22 [a phrase describing an elephant]
23 [a phrase describing a car]
24 [a phrase describing a skyscraper]
25 [a phrase describing a tree]
26 [a phrase describing an egg]
27 [a phrase describing a flower]
28 because/after
29 but/because
30 after/and
31 and/so
32 so/and
33 but
34 and/because
35 herd
36 adult
37 sleepy
38 cautious
39 error
40 soon

Paper 23

1 6
2 5
3 Freda
4 *The number of the house was Four*
5 *Marge and Millie shared the front room*
6 *The house belonged to the Council*
7–8 *e.g. They might get hurt, they might damage the house*
9–15
   chest, match, wave, tank, pen, ring, jam
16–19
   "It is time to go for a swim," called Tim.
20–23
   "Naomi has gone to sleep," whispered Dad.
24 dark<u>ness</u>
25 <u>dis</u>agree
26 reason<u>able</u>
27 <u>non</u>sense
28–29
   <u>anti</u>clock<u>wise</u>

30–31
   <u>un</u>treat<u>able</u>
32–36
   [a different adverb added to the end of each sentence, e.g. silently, noisily]
37 carrot
38 turnip
39 spinach
40 cabbage

Paper 24

1 winter
2 mistlethrush
3 in hedgerows
4 *wren*
5 *The skylark's song is thus described*
6 *Most living plants die back (lose their leaves etc.) in winter*
7–8 *The skylark, because the poet states it is 'loveliest of all'*
9 drink
10 hold
11 creep
12 forget
13 make
14 find
15 fly
16 wake
17–22

noun	verb	pronoun
Cardiff	walked	me
adjective	**adverb**	**conjunction**
brown	quickly	because

23 Daniel's rabbit
24 this girl's book
25 Mrs Thompson's hat
26 the milkman's overall
27 his wife's name
28 the wolves' howls
29 tractor
30 train
31 trampoline
32 trapeze
33 tray
34 (3)
35 (5)
36 (6)
37 (1)
38 (7)
39 (4)
40 (2)

Paper 13

James and Matthew took their money and chose their favourite horses. They stood watching the merry-go-round, and two horses seemed more beautiful than the others. Their names, printed in curly letters on their necks, were Fun and Spit Fire. They had scarlet saddles and their backs were painted in green and blue and cherry-red, with diamonds of scarlet and scrolls of gold. Their mouths were open, showing white teeth, and red tongues lolled out. Their gold eyes flashed, and their heads were thrown back in the speed of their running. They looked magnificent. The boys rode on these two all afternoon until their money was spent. It was grand to career on these galloping horses, with their red nostrils and their carved golden manes.

James and Matthew walked away, disappointed their time had come to an end. When, suddenly, Matthew's elbow was nudged, he turned to find himself face to face with Spit Fire, his gold eyes flashing with excitement.

Underline the right answers.

1 What were James and Matthew watching?
(a penny, a merry-go-round, a circus)

2 What colour were the horses' saddles?
(cherry-red, green, blue, scarlet)

3 Where were the names of the two horses written?
(on their chests, on their necks, on their saddles)

Answer these questions.

4–5 What two things were inside the horses' open mouths?
They had white teeth and red tongues.

6 Whose elbow was nudged?
Matthew's elbow was nudged.

7 Which word in the passage also means 'a feeling of happiness'?
exitiment

3

8 How do you think Matthew felt at the end of this passage?

I think Matthew felt he wanted to ride the horse again.

| | 5 |

Underline the correct **homophone** in the brackets.

9 It was a very happy (seen, ~~scene~~).

10 I have never (~~seen~~, scene) so many people there.

11 The (~~bough~~, bow) of the tree had broken off.

12 The man gave the queen a graceful (bough, ~~bow~~).

13 There was a big (~~hole~~, whole) in the ground.

14 The (hole, ~~whole~~) school went to see the play.

15 The dog ate the (meet, ~~meat~~) in his bowl.

16 Jess said she'd (~~meet~~, meat) Callum at the park.

| | 8 |

Write the following lines in a shortened form, using the apostrophe.

e.g. the glove belonging to the lady *the lady's glove*

17 the jeans worn by the girl *the girl's jeans*

18 the shoe belonging to my father *My father's shoe*

19 the toy the child had *The child's toy*

20 the paw of the dog *The dog's paw*

21 the pencil Ravi owned *Ravi's pencil*

22 the bracelet belonging to my gran *My gran's pencil*

| | 6 |

Write these words in **alphabetical order**.

storm   station   stick   study   stem   stranger

23 (1) _____   **24** (2) _____

25 (3) _____   **26** (4) _____

27 (5) _____   **28** (6) _____

| | 6 |

Underline the **adjectives** in each sentence.

29 The shaggy dog panted loudly.

30–31 Tom's bright blue coat suited him well.

32 The glistening raindrops hung on the branches.

33 Naomi slept in her cosy bed.

34–35 Donna's long, golden hair had all been cut off!

7

Write a more powerful **verb** for each of these verbs.

e.g. take   *grab*

36 say   _____   **37** look   _____

38 walk   _____   **39** call   _____

40 touch   _____

5

40
TOTAL

Paper 14

The next day was quite a different day. Instead of being hot and sunny, it was cold and misty. Pooh didn't mind for himself, but when he thought of all the honey the bees wouldn't be making, a cold and misty day always made him feel sorry for them. He said so to Piglet when Piglet came to fetch him, and Piglet said that he wasn't thinking of that so much, but of how cold and miserable it would be being lost all day and night on the top of the Forest. But when he and Pooh had got to Rabbit's house, Rabbit said it was just the day for them, because Tigger always bounced on ahead of everybody, and as soon as he got out of sight, they would hurry away in the other direction, and he would never see them again.

From *The House at Pooh Corner* by A A Milne

Underline the right answers.

1 The day was (hot and sunny, windy with showers, cold and misty).

2 Pooh was sorry for (Piglet, the bees, himself).

3 Piglet and Pooh went to (Rabbit's house, Tigger's house, Pooh's house).

Answer these questions.

4 Why did Pooh feel sorry for the bees?

_____

5 Which place was Piglet worried about being lost on?

_____

6 Who always went ahead of everyone else?

_____

7 What were the others going to do when Tigger got out of sight?

_____

8 How do you think Tigger would have felt?

_____

Using the **suffixes**, make two more words using each **root word**.

ness   ed   ly   ing

9–10 kind   _____   _____

11–12 blind   _____   _____

13–14 jump   _____   _____

15–16 correct   _____   _____

Rewrite these sentences, writing the words in bold in their **plural** form.

17–18 The **knife is** sharp.

_____

19–20 The **woman** picked up the **child**.

_____

21–22 The **leaf was** yellow.

_____

23–26 Your **foot is** too big for **this slipper**.

_____

10

Copy these book titles, adding the missing capital letters.

27–29 adventures at longley farm

_____

30–31 flying machines _____

5

School Trip

Line up
search in panic
for partner on the coach.
An odd number – one left over
Why me?

by Tracey Blance

Answer these questions.

32 What is this child looking for?

_____

33 What vehicle is taking the class on their school trip?

_____

34 Did the child find a partner?

_____

35 How do you think he/she felt?

4

_____

Finish these sentences by adding a more interesting word than the word in brackets.

36 The party was _____ . (nice)

37 Moira had a _____ time at the park. (good)

38 Bob's clothes looked _____ . (nice)

39 Sandy _____ a camera. (got)

40 Mum _____ the cake just in time. (got)

Paper 15

It was a high, piercing sound, almost like the yelping of a dog. Jai stopped picking the wild strawberries that grew in the grass around him, and looked up at the sky. He had a dog – a shaggy guard dog called Motu – but Motu did not yet yelp, he growled and barked. The strange sound came from the sky, and Jai had heard it before. Now realising what it was, he jumped to his feet, calling to his dog, calling his sheep to start for home. Motu came bounding towards him, ready for a game.

"Not now, Motu!" said Jai. "We must get the lambs home quickly."

Again he looked up at the sky.

He saw it now, a black speck against the sun, growing larger as it circled the mountain, coming lower every moment – a Golden Eagle, king of the skies over the Himalayas, ready now to swoop and seize its prey.

From *The Eyes of the Eagle* by Ruskin Bond

Underline the right answers.

1 What was the 'high, piercing sound' like?
(a call, a dog, a bird)

2 What was Jai doing when he heard the sound?
(counting sheep, playing with Motu, picking strawberries)

3 Where did the sound come from?
(the bushes, the sky, he didn't know)

3

Answer these questions.

4 When Jai called Motu, what did Motu think he wanted?

_____

5 How is the Golden Eagle described in the passage?

_____

6 Why do you think Jai wanted to get the lambs home quickly?

3

_____

7 Which word in the passage shows that the creature hunted for food?

_____

8–9 Write two words describing how Jai would have felt when he spotted the Golden Eagle.

3

_____   _____

Write this sentence again, adding the missing punctuation and capital letter.

10–15 have you seen my hat called Wendy going to the door

_____

6

_____

Add the missing apostrophes to these **plural nouns**.

e.g. the six boys books   _the six boys' books_

16 the three dogs collars   _____

17 the five girls socks   _____

18 the nine hens eggs   _____

19 the two cats bowls   _____

20 the four dolls beds   _____

21 the five boys footballs   _____

7

22 the three spiders webs   _____

Next to each **verb** write two **adverbs** that could describe it.

23–24 walk _____ _____

25–26 sleep _____ _____

27–28 eat _____ _____

29–30 draw _____ _____

Write five words with *wa* to match each picture.

31

32

33

34

35

Underline a **synonym** for the word in bold.

36 fell	dropped	flew	rose	felt
37 rush	blow	bump	knock	hurry
38 unlike	different	same	unkind	similar
39 beneath	above	beyond	away	under
40 choose	like	eat	select	present

Paper 16

Underline the right answers.

1 What is special about these shoes?
(They hover, they are difficult to walk in, they make your feet sore)

2 How much do the shoes cost?
(£9.99, £99.99, £999.99)

2

Answer these questions.

3–4 Give two reasons why people might want to buy Hover Shoes.

_____

_____

5 What line in the advert tells us that Hover Shoes are a new invention?

_____

6 Why do you think the advert says 'Everyone wants them'?

_____

7 Would you like a pair of Hover Shoes? Why?

_____

5

Write each of these **nouns** in their plural form.

8 banana _____   **9** fox _____

10 lorry _____   **11** tray _____

12 church _____   **13** brush _____

14 girl _____   **15** beach _____

8

Add the missing comma to each of these sentences.

16 We must get in the car otherwise we will get wet.

17 Daniel's grandmother could do a little magic but not much.

18 She was very unhappy but her face didn't show it.

19 The dog ran on ahead desperately looking for his home.

20 Fran dozed off her eyes drowsy with sleep.

21 Groping in the dark Sam found the light switch.

`6`

Underline the feminine word for the word in bold.

22 prince	fairy	woman	princess	queen
23 duke	player	actress	lady	duchess
24 husband	mother	father	wife	aunt
25 uncle	nephew	aunt	niece	sister
26 he	her	him	them	she
27 nephew	uncle	niece	cousin	woman
28 brother	sister	mother	child	twin

`7`

Underline the **adjectival phrase** (group of words describing a noun) in each sentence.

29 The large, brown clock hung on the wall.

30 The bright, loud, flashing fireworks exploded in the air.

31 Sam, the long-haired, shaggy dog loved going for a walk.

32 The stern, pale-faced teacher glared at the children.

33 Caroline's coat, soaked and muddy, didn't look new any more.

34 Rain poured from the grey, heavy clouds.

`6`

Use each of these **pronouns** in a sentence.

35 I

42

36 ours

_____

37 him

_____

38 mine

_____

39 they

_____

40 she

_____

Paper 17

The following morning we gathered our stores together, packed all we could into bags, and fixed these across the backs of the animals. The fowls were coaxed into the tent with some handfuls of corn, and then we put them safely into two hampers.

The stores that we could not carry were packed into the tent, and casks and chests piled round for protection.

We formed a strange procession. My wife and Fritz led the way. Then came the laden cow and ass. Jack, with the monkey on his shoulder, drove the goats. Ernest managed the sheep, and I came last, while Turk and Bill seemed happy in guarding us all.

We travelled slowly across the bridge, and when any animals were tempted to stray, to eat the rich grass, the dogs brought them back to an orderly line.

Underline the right answers.

1–2 The stores were put (in a chest, on the backs of animals, in hampers, in a tent).

3 (Fritz, Ernest, Jack, Turk) and the narrator's wife led the way.

4 (Fritz, Ernest, Jack, Turk) took an animal on his shoulder.

Answer these questions.

5 How were the fowls coaxed into the tent?

_____

6 What happened if any animals were tempted to stray?

_____

7 Write a definition of the word 'procession'.

_____

8 Why do you think they travelled slowly across the bridge?

_____

Circle words that are **nouns**.

9–16 gatepost   happy   bunch   laughed

Wednesday   greasy   sadly   Tom

Edinburgh   Edward   freedom

stream   famous   fought

Rewrite these sentences, adding the missing speech marks.

17 Come quickly! screamed Sam.

_____

18 How are you, Gran? asked Peter.

_____

19 It's time to go, sighed Mum.

_____

20 This way to the Tunnel of Screams, directed the attendant.

_____

21 Have we got time? enquired Nancy.

_____

22 Where are my slippers? exclaimed Grandad.

_____

Choose the most suitable **adverb** from the words below to put in each space.

cheerfully   roughly   gently   stiffly   loudly

23 The soldier stood _____ to attention.

24 The nurse removed the dressing _____ .

25 The ducks in the pond quacked _____ .

26 The old man _____ greeted his friend.

27 The boys pushed past her _____ .

Add the **suffix** _ion_ to each word, but be careful as some letters may need to be altered.

e.g.   explode + ion = _explosion_

28 express + ion   =   _____

29 instruct + ion   =   _____

30 subtract + ion   =   _____

31 collide + ion   =   _____

32 educate + ion   =   _____

33 pollute + ion   =   _____

Write an **antonym** of each word.

34 happy   _____

35 large   _____

36 catch   _____

37 noisy   _____

38 thin   _____

39 above   _____

40 down   _____

Paper 18

Read the following passage and then write **true** or **false** against each statement.

When she was only three years old, Maria Celli loved to play the violin. By the time she was five, she was having violin lessons from a master who thought she was extremely clever. Her parents were very proud of Maria, and they loved to hear her play. When she was eighteen she gave her first concert in London.

1 Maria started to play the piano when she was five. _____

2 Maria was taught the violin by a master. _____

3 Maria didn't like playing the violin. _____

4 Her parents were very proud of her. _____

5 She gave her first concert in London. _____

6 She gave her first concert when she was five. _____

7 Her parents taught her to play the piano. _____

8 Her parents loved to hear her play. _____

9 Her master thought that she was very clever. _____

9

Put one of the **conjunctions** in each of the spaces below.

but   although   than   and   if   so

10 He tried to open the door _____ he had seen the man lock it.

11 I would rather have a cup of hot tea _____ drink a mug of cold coffee.

12 I cut my hand _____ I put a plaster on it.

13 Joe wanted to buy some sweets _____ he hadn't brought enough money.

14 I shall wear a T-shirt _____ it is a warm day.

15 The girls are going camping _____ the boys want to go too.

6

46

Rewrite these words, drawing a line to separate the **syllables**.

e.g. yellow   *yel//low*

16 bubble _____   17 paddle _____

18 flannel _____   19 kennel _____

20 arrive _____   21 saddle _____

22 burrow _____   23 cabbage _____

8

Complete this table of comparing **adjectives**.

24–31

	add 'er'	**add 'est'**
short		
high		
small		
slow		

8

Write these words in **alphabetical order**.

mint   mince   minute   minister

32 (1) _____   33 (2) _____

34 (3) _____   35 (4) _____

4

With a line match the words that have the same letter string (group of letters) but which make a different sound.

36 snow   have

37 pull   trough

38 ear   skull

39 wave   cow

40 bough   wear

5

40
TOTAL

Paper 19

Billy Doesn't Like School Really

Billy doesn't like school really.
It's not because he can't do the work
but because some of the other kids
don't seem to like him that much.

They call him names
and make up jokes about his mum.

Everyone laughs . . . except Billy.
Everyone laughs . . . except Billy.

They all think it's OK
because it's only a laugh and a joke
and they don't really mean it anyway
but Billy doesn't know that.

Billy doesn't know that
and because of that
Billy doesn't like school really.

by Paul Cookson

Underline the right answers.

1 Does Billy like school?
(yes, no, don't know)

2 How many children don't like Billy?
(all of them, some of them, none of them)

2

Answer these questions.

3 Who doesn't laugh in this poem?

_____

4–5 What two things do the other children do to Billy?

_____

6 Why do all the children think it is OK to have a laugh and a joke?

_____

7–9 Write three words describing how you would feel if you were Billy.

_____   _____   _____

Write the two small words each **compound word** is made from.

10 handbag   = _____ + _____

11 sunlight   = _____ + _____

12 candlestick   = _____ + _____

13 shoelace   = _____ + _____

14 toothpaste   = _____ + _____

15 dustbin   = _____ + _____

16 postman   = _____ + _____

Write these words, depending on their **prefix**, in the table below.

deflate   replay   demist   prehistoric   revisit   precaution

17–22

re	de	pre

Write each of these phrases in a sentence and don't forget the missing apostrophe.

23–24 this birds chicks

_____

25–26 that girls sweets

_____

27–28 those boys pencils

_____

49

Antony likes outdoor games; he is very popular with the other boys, and he is untidy and noisy. Brian is artistic and he likes making things. He is neat and quiet.

Underline the correct sentences.

29–33 Antony likes playing football.
Brian's books are not very tidy.
Brian likes painting.
Antony is a quiet, tidy boy.
Brian likes craft lessons.
The other boys like Antony.
Antony would rather do woodwork than play cricket.
Brian is often told he must not make so much noise.
Antony would rather play cricket than stay indoors.

5

Copy any **nouns**, **adjectives**, **verbs** and **adverbs** found in the sentence below.

34–40 While walking briskly on a windy Thursday I heard a loud scream.

nouns _____

adjectives _____

verbs _____

adverbs _____

7

40
TOTAL

Paper 20

They fetched the Christmas tree from the market; and Sarah couldn't wait to start decorating it. Mum got the box of decorations down from the loft, and brushed the cobwebs from it. First they took out the fairy lights, and plugged them in. They worked, so Mum wound them around the tree. Next came tinsel, silver and red, and coloured glass balls. Sarah was very fond of them. They were the same ones every year, unless one was broken. When the tree was finished, Sarah stood on a chair and carefully put the fairy on top.

Underline the right answers.

1 They bought the tree from a (shop, market, lorry).

2 The colours of the (glass balls, tinsel, tree, fairy) were silver and red.

3 The last decoration to go up was (the tinsel, the lights, the fairy).

`3`

Answer these questions.

4 Where did Mum get the box of decorations from?

_____

5 Which decoration was put on the tree first?

_____

6 What decoration was Sarah 'very fond of'?

_____

`3`

7–8 Write two words describing how Sarah might have felt while decorating the Christmas tree.

_____   _____

9 Name another festival when people decorate their houses.

_____

`3`

Underline the **noun** or nouns in each sentence which use the same word in their **plural** and **singular form**.

10 The aircraft flew high in the sky.

11–12 The fish swam quickly, darting through the seaweed.

13 The tourists watched the bison from their coach.

14 The steep Welsh slopes are home to the sheep.

`5`

Write an *dge* word that matches each picture.

15   16   17

_____   _____   _____

51

18   **19**   **20**

_____ _____ _____

Put a question mark or exclamation mark at the end of each sentence.

21 Catch the thief_____

22 Shall we look in this shop_____

23 Don't do that_____

24 Why does Dad snore so loudly_____

25 Can we go swimming now_____

26 Hurry up, time is running out_____

27 Listen, a siren_____

28 Please may I have a sweet_____

Circle the words that wouldn't have been used a hundred years ago.

29–34 camcorder CD player donkey

cinema doctor astronaut television

candle microwave cloth

Put the **pronouns** in the correct columns in the table.

me yours hers I mine theirs

35–40

Pronouns about others	Pronouns about myself

6

8

6

6

40
TOTAL

52

Paper 21

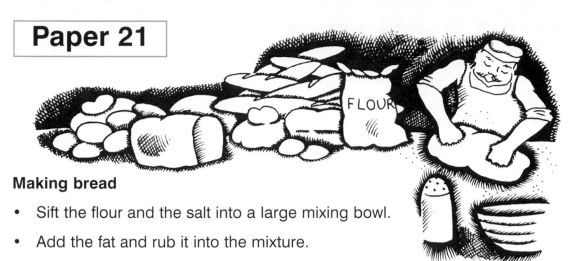

Making bread

- Sift the flour and the salt into a large mixing bowl.

- Add the fat and rub it into the mixture.

- Make a hollow in the centre of the ingredients.

- Measure the water very carefully into another bowl. The water should be hand-hot (in other words you should be able to hold a finger in it with comfort).

- Stir in the sugar and then sprinkle the yeast on to it. Set aside in a warm place for about ten minutes.

- Then pour the yeast mixture quickly into the centre of the flour.

- Use both hands to mix it all to a dough.

- Turn it out on to a board and knead the dough for about ten minutes.

Underline the right answers.

1–2 Which two ingredients are added first to the flour?
(salt, sugar, fat, yeast)

3 How hot should the water be?
(boiling, hand-hot, warm, cold)

Answer these questions.

4–5 Which two ingredients are added to the water?

_____   _____

6–7 What two things are you told to do for ten minutes?

_____

_____

3

8 After the dough has been kneaded, what else needs to be done before the bread can be eaten?

_____

5

Add the missing commas in each sentence.

9–10 Aman has to buy carrots potatoes rice and tomatoes at the shop.

11–13 At the park Geri Meena David Jason and John all play together.

14–15 On Mark's way to school he passes the police station the swimming pool the park and the shops.

16–17 At the farm the children fed the goats stroked the pigs milked the cows and brushed the horse.

9

Complete this table of comparing **adjectives**. Some words need their last letter doubled before adding the suffix.

18–25

	add 'er'	add 'est'
hot		
tall		
big		
thin		

8

Complete each word to make a **diminutive**.

ling   let   ock

26 drop_____   **27** duck_____

28 bull_____   **29** book_____

4

Write this sentence again, adding the missing punctuation and capital letters.

30–35 is it time jess got out of bed asked her brother

_____

_____

6

Write *their* or *there* in each of the spaces below. Don't forget to start with a capital letter if necessary.

36 The children went to play with _____ friends in the swimming pool.

37 _____ isn't going to be any rain today.

38–39 _____ shoes are over _____ on the floor.

40 _____ was a huge bang as the fireworks exploded.

Paper 22

Sounds like Magic
I listened to a sea-shell
and thought I could hear
the rushing of the waves
inside my ear.

I held an empty egg-shell
close against my head
and thought I heard a pecking chick
hatching from its bed.

I found a hollow coconut
and listened for a sound
and thought I heard horses' hooves
pounding on the ground.

I took an empty teacup
to see what I might hear
and thought I heard a giant's voice
booming in my ear.

by Celia Warren

Underline the right answers.

1–2 A sea-shell, (an egg-shell, a coconut, a mug, a bucket) and a teacup are all listened to in the poem.

3 (A pecking chick, Horses' hooves, Rushing waves) could be heard in the sea-shell.

Answer these questions.

4 What was heard in the hollow coconut?

_____

5 What was the booming sound like?

_____

6–7 Write two verbs found in the poem.

_____   _____

8 Why do you think the poet has written about a chick pecking?

_____

Add the **suffix** *ship* or *hood* to each of these words.

9 friend_____   10 neighbour_____

11 mother_____   12 apprentice_____

Add *its* or *it's* to fill the gap in each sentence. Don't forget to start with a capital letter if necessary.

13 _____ a beautiful day.

14 The cat played with _____ ball.

15–16 _____ time you remembered your own bag, _____ not that hard!

17 Everyone was lined up outside the school; _____ fire alarm was going.

18 Will's dog lost _____ ball.

19 _____ got to be here somewhere!

20 _____ been a brilliant party. I wish I could have one every week!

Write a **phrase** (group of words) that could describe each of these **nouns**.

e.g. bed   *the soft, feathery, comfortable bed*

21 **coat** _____

22 **elephant** _____

23 **car** _____

24 **skyscraper** _____

25 **tree** _____

26 **egg** _____

27 **flower** _____

Use one of the following **conjunctions** in each gap.

                    but   and   so   after   because

28 I missed the train _____ I overslept.

29 Ahmed is in the cricket team _____ Josh wasn't good enough.

30 Mum wrapped up my present _____ I went to bed.

31 Jake bought some toffees _____ Mike got some too.

32 Cathy's sewing is untidy _____ she will have to do it again.

33 I like macaroni _____ my brother likes spaghetti better.

34 The sky was blue _____ the sun was shining.

Match the words to their **definitions**.

            soon   sleepy   error   cautious   herd   adult

35 group of cattle   _____

36 grown-up   _____

37 heavy-eyed   _____

38 careful   _____

39 mistake   _____

40 in a short time   _____

Paper 23

It is very difficult to think of anything nicer to share between six children than an empty house. Number Four had, of course, the same number of rooms as the other houses in the Lane, the two bedrooms upstairs, the front room, the kitchen, and the scullery sticking out at the back, which was almost a room each, and that is how they divided up the house. The front room was given to Marge and Millie to share, and the other rooms divided naturally. Freda had the kitchen, because she liked cooking things. Dickie had the scullery, because he was messy with his carpentering. Sally and Dave each had a bedroom. Of course, the children were not really allowed into Number Four, which belonged to the Council. It had never been said that they were not to go in; it was just known that they could not, and that was where the especial charm of the house lay, because they had found their own way in, and nobody knew anything about it.

From *The Children of Primrose Lane* by Noel Streatfeild

Underline the right answers.

1 How many children shared the empty house?
(3, 4, 5, 6, 7)

2 How many rooms were there in the empty house?
(3, 4, 5, 6, 7)

3 Which child liked cooking things?
(Sally, Dave, Freda, Marge)

Answer these questions.

4 What was the number of the house the children played in?

_____

5 Which children shared the front room?

_____

6 Who did the house belong to?

_____

3

7–8 Give two reasons why the children shouldn't play in the house.

_____

_____

`5`

Circle the **homonyms**.

9–15   chest   hat   match   wave   jacket   tank

          pen   ring   dog   gate   jam   desk

`7`

Rewrite these sentences, adding the missing speech marks, commas and full-stops.

16–19 It is time to go for a swim called Tim

_____

19–23 Naomi has gone to sleep whispered Dad

_____

`8`

Underline the **prefixes** and **suffixes** in these words.

24 darkness   **25** disagree   **26** reasonable

27 nonsense   **28–29** anticlockwise   **30–31** untreatable

`8`

Add a different **adverb** to each sentence.

32 The children entered the hall _____.

33 The children entered the hall _____.

34 The children entered the hall _____.

35 The children entered the hall _____.

36 The children entered the hall _____.

`5`

Add the missing **vowel letters** to each word to make a vegetable.

37 c__rr__t   **38** t__rn__p

39 sp__n__ch   **40** c__bb__g__

`4`

40
TOTAL

Paper 24

Songs

When everything else is silent
in the dead of winter,
there are still some birds singing.
Perched on a bare branch, the mistlethrush
braves the snowstorm with a wild song,
bold robin pipes up cheerily every day;
on dull afternoons, a couple of starlings
whistle and chuckle on rooftops,
the nervous wren, skulking in hedgerows,
surprises with a loud voice.
Loveliest of all, when mornings are calm,
a few notes of pure silver drop from the skies
where a single skylark hovers in sunlight,
as far away as springtime
and all its choirs of sweet singers.

by Leonard Clark

Underline the right answers.

1 Which season is this poem set in?
(spring, summer, autumn, winter)

2 Which bird braves the snowstorm?
(cuckoo, wren, mistlethrush, skylark)

3 Where does the wren hide?
(in hedgerows, on rooftops, on bare branches)

3

Answer these questions.

4 Which bird has a 'loud voice'?

_____

5 Which bird song is described as 'notes of pure silver'?

_____

6 Why do you think the word 'dead' would be used to describe winter?

_____

7–8 Which bird do you think Leonard Clark likes the best? Why?

_____

_____

5

Put these **verbs** in the **present tense**.

9 drank _____ **10** held _____

11 crept _____ **12** forgot _____

13 made _____ **14** found _____

15 flew _____ **16** woke _____

8

Write each word in the correct column in the table.

Cardiff   because   me   walked   quickly   brown

17–22

noun	verb	pronoun	adjective	adverb	conjunction

6

Add the missing apostrophe to these **nouns**.

23 D a n i e l s r a b b i t

24 t h i s g i r l s b o o k

25 M r s T h o m p s o n s h a t

26 t h e m i l k m a n s o v e r a l l

27 h i s w i f e s n a m e

28 t h e w o l v e s h o w l s

6

Put these words in **alphabetical order**.

train   trapeze   tractor   trampoline   tray

29 (1) _____ **30** (2) _____

31 (3) _____   **32** (4) _____

33 (5) _____

Write the number that matches the expression with its meaning.

34	a wet blanket	_____	(1) not very well
35	a bookworm	_____	(2) full of energy and high spirits
36	a copy-cat	_____	(3) a miserable person
37	off colour	_____	(4) very slowly
38	as the crow flies	_____	(5) a keen reader
39	at a snail's pace	_____	(6) someone who imitates another
40	full of beans	_____	(7) the most direct way

First published in 1973 by:
Thomas Nelson and Sons Ltd

This edition in 2001 by:
Nelson Thornes Ltd
Delta Place
27 Bath Road
CHELTENHAM
GL53 7TH
United Kingdom

05 / 10 9 8 7

A catalogue record for this book is available from the British Library

ISBN 0-7487-6182-9

Illustrations by R. Barton and K. Kett
Page make-up by Aetos Ltd

Printed in Croatia by Zrinski

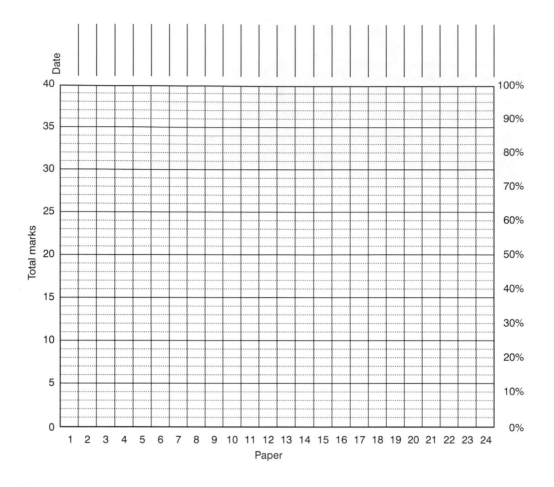

Acknowledgements
The authors and publishers wish to thank the following for permission to use copyright material: extract from *Lost – One Pair of Legs* from The Last Slice of the Rainbow by Joan Aiken, Copyright © Joan Aiken Enterprises Ltd; extract from *Blitz* by Robert Westall, © the Estate of Robert Westall 1995, permission granted by the author's estate; extract from *The House at Pooh Corner*, © A.A. Milne, copyright under the Berne Convention, published by Methuen, an imprint of Egmont Children's books Limited, London and used with permission; 'School Trip' by Tracey Blance, © Tracey Blance 2000, reprinted by permission of the author; 'Billy Doesn't Like School Really' by Paul Cookson; 'Sounds like Magic' by Celia Warren; extract from *The Children of Primrose Lane* (Copyright © Noel Streatfeild 1947) reproduced by permission of A M Heath & Co. Ltd; 'Songs' by Leonard Clark, reproduced by permission of The Literary Executor of Leonard Clark.

Every effort has been made to trace all copyright holders, but if any have been inadvertently overlooked the publishers will be pleased to make the necessary arrangements at the first opportunity.